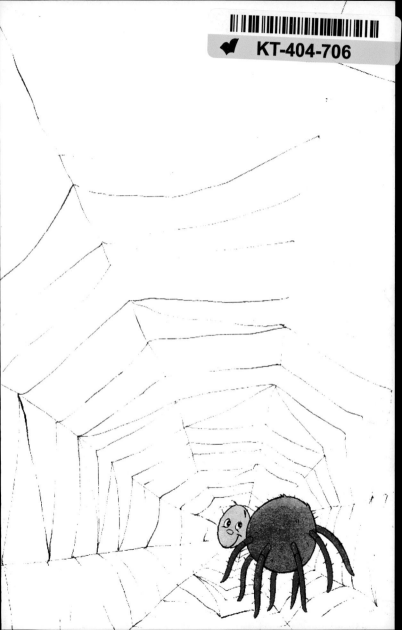

© 1997 Owl Records Ltd
Published by Geddes & Grosset, an imprint of
Children's Leisure Products Limited,
David Dale House, New Lanark, ML11 9DJ, Scotland,
for Owl Records Ltd, Dublin, Ireland

First printed 1997
Reprinted 1998, 1999, 2000

ISBN 1 85534 780 6

Printed and bound in Slovenia

IRISH LEGENDS

Finn
and the
Wicked Fairy of Tara

Retold by Reg Keating
Illustrated by Heather McKay

Tarantula Books

Cumhall was the leader of a great band of warriors. They were called the Fianna.

Cumhall had a young son called Finn. Finn could run as fast as a hare. He could swim like a fish. He could hunt in the darkest forest and he could fish in the deepest river.

Most important of all, he was kind and gentle, and helped other people.

When his father died, Finn wanted to be leader of the Fianna.

Before he could do this, he had to find the bag of treasure that had been stolen from his father.

Finn set off to find the bag of treasure. He brought his dog, Bran, with him.

Bran was a big hairy dog. He liked to go hunting with Finn. He was very good at finding things. He would sniff and sniff until he smelled what he was looking for.

Soon Bran was on the scent of the bag of treasure. He sniffed and sniffed, and he got closer and closer.

Bran found the bag of treasure in the long grass beside a high mountain.

Finn was very happy. He told Bran he was a very good dog.

Suddenly, the mountain began to shake. Finn looked up and saw a huge giant running down from the top of the mountain.

"You stole my treasure!" roared the giant.

"It is not your treasure," replied Finn. "You stole it from my father."

The giant did not listen to Finn.

"I will fight you for the treasure," he roared.

Finn was much smaller than the giant. But he was also much faster and much wiser.

Soon, Finn defeated the wicked giant. He picked up the bag of treasure and set off for Tara.

T ara is where the King of Ireland lived.

When Finn arrived at Tara, it was Halloween.

In olden days, Halloween was a ghostly time. Ghosts and wicked fairies came out at midnight on Halloween.

Aillen was the most wicked fairy of all. Every Halloween, Aillen would come out at midnight.

He would play beautiful music on a magic flute. His music made everyone very sleepy.

When everyone was asleep, Aillen would burn the king's castle to the ground with flames from his mouth.

Every year, the king would order his best soldiers to guard the castle. It made no difference. Aillen's music always made them fall asleep.

"Can no one save my castle from this wicked fairy?" the king asked sadly.

"I can," said Finn, but the soldiers laughed at him. If they could not protect the castle, how could Finn? He was just a little boy.

The king was desperate. He listened to what Finn had to say and decided to give him a chance.

"If you can save my castle," said the king, "then you shall be leader of the Fianna."

L ater that night, Finn guarded the castle on his own, except for Bran, of course.

At midnight, Finn heard soft, sweet music in the distance. It was Aillen and his magic flute.

The music grew louder and louder. Soon, Finn began to fall asleep.

Bran saw what was happening and gave a little bark. At once, Finn woke up and saw Aillen, the wicked fairy, coming towards him.

Quickly, Finn opened his bag of treasure and took out a magic cap. He put the magic cap on his head and pulled it over his ears.

With the magic cap over his ears, Finn could no longer hear the music and was able to stay awake.

Finn watched as Aillen came out from the bushes.

When Aillen saw that Finn was not asleep, he was very angry.

He rushed at Finn, with flames coming out of his mouth.

These flames were very, very hot. They burnt everything that they touched. They burned the grass and they burned the trees. They even burned the stones on the roadway leading up to the castle.

Finn hid behind his shield to protect himself from the flames.

Then he took a spear from his bag of treasure. This was a special spear, which fire could not burn or melt.

Finn waited and waited for the right moment. It was getting hotter and hotter.

Just before his shield was about to melt, Finn threw the spear at the wicked fairy.

The spear went straight through the flames. It hit Aillen in the shoulder.

The wicked fairy screamed and disappeared into thin air. He was never seen again.

The king was very happy. Never again would the wicked fairy destroy his castle.

The king kept his promise and Finn became the leader of the Fianna.